English Practice for

Year 1

Ages 5-6

This book belongs to:

English Year 1, Book 1

Scholastic Education, an imprint of Scholastic Ltd
Book End, Range Road, Witney, Oxfordshire, OX29 0YD
Registered office: Westfield Road, Southam, Warwickshire CV47 0RA
www.scholastic.co.uk

© 2015, Scholastic Ltd

3 4 5 6 7 8 9   6 7 8 9 0 1 2 3 4 5

British Library Cataloguing-in-Publication Data
A catalogue record for this book is available from the British Library.

ISBN 978-1407-14193-0
Printed in Malaysia

Editorial
Rachel Morgan, Melissa Somers, Sarah Sodhi, Catherine Baker and Zoe Clarke

Design
Scholastic Design Team: Neil Salt, Nicolle Thomas
and Oxford Designers & Illustrators Ltd

Cover Design
Neil Salt

Illustration
Cathy Hughes

Acknowledgements
The publishers gratefully acknowledge permission to reproduce the following copyright material: **Colin and Jacqui Hawkins** for the use of an extract from *Tog the Dog* by Colin and Jacqui Hawkins. Text © 1986, Colin and Jacqui Hawkins (1986, Pat and Pals Ltd). Every effort has been made to trace copyright holders for the works reproduced in this book, and the publishers apologise for any inadvertent omissions.

Contents

Why buy this book?

This series has been designed to support the introduction of the new National Curriculum in schools in England. The new curriculum is more challenging in English and includes the requirement for children's understanding to be secure before moving on. These practice books will help your child practise all of the skills they will learn at school, including some topics they might not have encountered previously.

How to use this book

- The content is divided into National Curriculum topics (for example, Spelling, Grammar, Comprehension and so on). Find out what your child is doing in school and dip into the relevant practice activities as required.

- Let your child know you are sharing the activities and support if necessary using the helpful quick tips at the top of most pages.

- Keep the working time short and come back to an activity if your child finds it too difficult. Ask your child to note any areas of difficulty. Don't worry if your child does not 'get' a concept first time, as children learn at different rates and content is likely to be covered throughout the school year.

- Check your child's answers using the answers section at the end of this book.

- Give lots of encouragement and tick off the progress chart as your child completes each chapter.

How to use the book

This tells you which topic you're working on.

This is the title of the activity.

Missing letters
All these words are missing something. Fill in the gaps using **ai**, **oi**, **ay** or **oy**.

r_____

sn_____l

b_____

c_____n

The snake's dinner
Some sounds are written down as two letters. For example: **ee**, **ae**, **ie**. But sometimes the two letters are not written together – there is another letter in between.
The /**ay**/ sound is sometimes spelled **a–e** as in **rake**.
Look at the spelling pattern **a–e** in the following words.
cake made late wave
Say the words out loud. The **a–e** make a long /**ay**/ sound.

Look at sn**a**k**e**. He's eaten all of the words with **a–e**! Write the missing letters in these words and say them out loud.

b__k__

sh__p__

g__m__

t__k__

sn__k__

sk__t__

Letters in slashes (like this) tell you it's the sound and not the spelling.

These boxes will help you with the activity.

The alien planet
Describe this picture. The words below will help you.

near   inside   in front of   beside
down   across   behind

The rocket has landed _____ a
volcano. A spaceman walks _____
the steps to get to the space buggy. Some aliens are
watching from _____ the rocks. They
live _____ the craters. The spaceman
is going to walk _____ the ground
to put a flag _____ some large rocks
_____ the aliens.

What did they say?
Look at the pictures showing the story of The Three Billy Goats Gruff. Using short sentences, write in the speech bubbles what the goats and the troll might be saying!

This is the instruction text. It tells you what to do.

Follow the instruction to complete the activity.

You might have to write on lines, in boxes, draw or circle things.

If you need help, ask an adult!

Pick the ending

Some sounds are spelled with a double letter at the end of words. For example:

/f/ is spelled **ff** in words such as **fluff**.

/s/ is spelled **ss** in words such as **boss**.

/z/ is spelled **zz** in words such as **jazz**.

/l/ is spelled **ll** in words such as **call**.

/k/ is spelled **ck** in words such as **back**.

Match the beginning of the words to the end of the words. Then write the word in the spaces. Use the pictures to help you. The first one has been done for you.

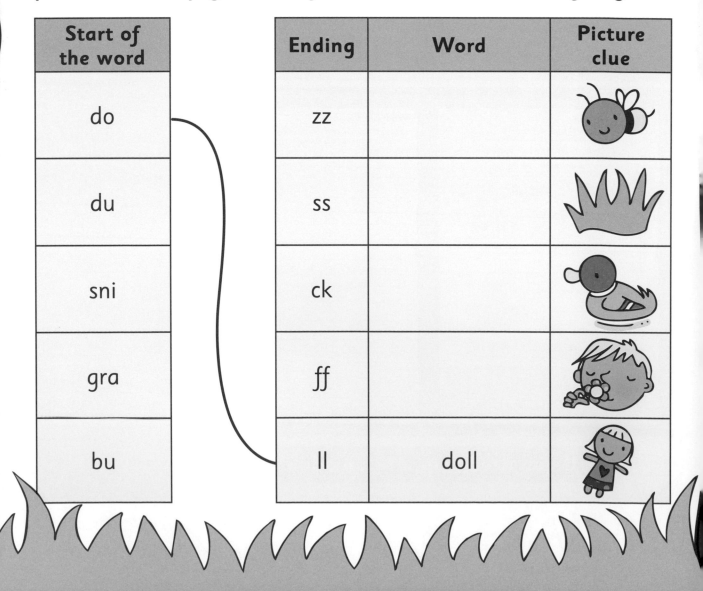

Start of the word		Ending	Word	Picture clue
do		zz		
du		ss		
sni		ck		
gra		ff		
bu		ll	doll	

Clap your hands to the animal beat!

Some words can be broken down into smaller bits, called **syllables**. To work out how many syllables a word has, try clapping when you say the word out loud.
Say the word **monkey**. You should have clapped your hands twice: **mon + key**. **Monkey** has two syllables.

How many syllables do these animals have? Write your answer in the space provided. Then add some animals of your own and draw them.

Word	Number of syllables	Drawing
rabbit	2	
butterfly	_____	
crocodile	_____	
elephant	_____	
caterpillar	_____	
_____	_____	
_____	_____	

Missing letters

All these words are missing something. Fill in the gaps using **ai**, **oi**, **ay** or **oy**.

r_____

sn_____l

b_____

c_____n

The snake's dinner

Some sounds are written down as two letters. For example: **ee**, **ae**, **ie**. But sometimes the two letters are not written together – there is another letter in between.

The /**ay**/ sound is sometimes spelled **a–e** as in **rake**.

Look at the spelling pattern **a–e** in the following words.

cake   made   late   wave

Say the words out loud. The **a–e** make a long /**ay**/ sound.

Look at sn**a**k**e**. He's eaten all of the words with **a–e**!
Write the missing letters in these words and say them out loud.

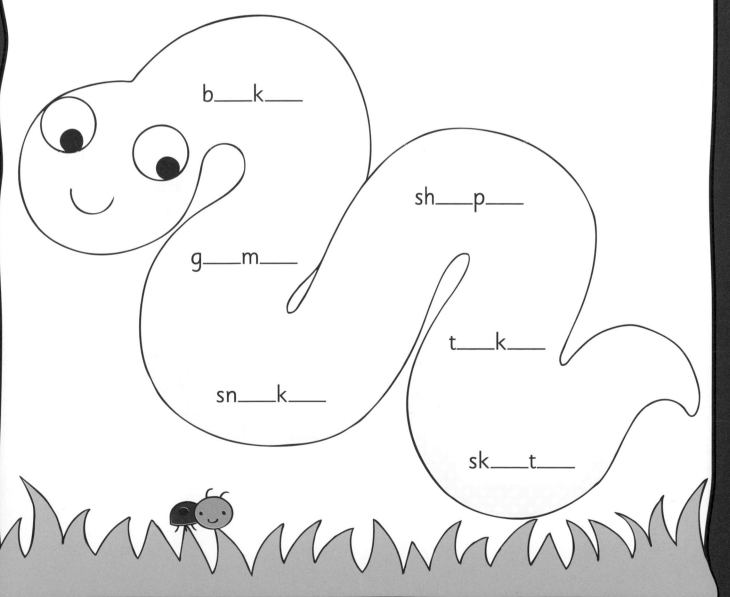

b___k___

sh___p___

g___m___

t___k___

sn___k___

sk___t___

Spelling

Find the word

Some sounds are written down as two letters. For example: **ee**, **ae**, **ie**. But sometimes the two letters are not written together – there is another letter in between.
The /**igh**/ sound is sometimes spelled **i–e** as in **ride**.

Look at the spelling pattern **i–e** in the following words.

| f**i**v**e** | l**i**k**e** | t**i**m**e** | s**i**d**e** | r**i**d**e** | l**i**m**e** | h**i**d**e** | b**i**k**e** |

Find these words hidden in the puzzle below. The words are hidden across or down.

r	i	d	e	p	f	j	x	r	q
o	k	a	d	h	b	o	f	c	a
j	m	f	e	k	p	l	i	k	e
f	r	i	j	l	a	h	m	o	e
p	z	v	o	i	c	i	g	f	b
g	s	e	k	m	s	d	t	r	s
f	b	s	b	e	u	e	x	v	i
b	i	k	e	m	r	c	e	p	d
l	d	n	p	r	e	n	q	f	e
t	i	m	e	a	i	x	d	e	n

What's on the line?

Some sounds are written down as two letters. For example: **ee**, **ae**, **ie**. But sometimes the two letters are not written together – there is another letter in between.
The /**oa**/ sound is spelled **o–e** in **home**.

Look at the words on the t-shirts hanging from the r**o**p**e**.
Colour in the t-shirts with the **o–e** words.

note

stone

bike

hope

rake

nose

Spot the word

Some sounds are written down as two letters. For example: **ee**, **ae**, **ie**, **ue**. But sometimes the two letters are not written together – there is another letter in between.
The /**oo**/ sound is sometimes spelled **u–e** as in **rule**.

Can you spot the **u–e** words here? Write the **u–e** words in the cube and stick the **ue** words in the glue.

blue   cute   huge   true   due   tune

clue   rule   cue   fuse   tube

CUBE

_____

_____

_____

_____

_____

GLUE

_____

_____

_____

_____

See a leaf

The spelling **ee** makes a long /**ee**/ sound.
For example: **see** and **free**
The letters **ea** and **ie** also make the long /**ee**/ sound in some words.
For example: **leaf** and **brief**.

Read the words. Circle the words that have a long /**ee**/ sound.

need   peas

field   tie   seal

net   chief   wheel   peel

easy   pet   tea   pin   team

piece   deep

Tell me

The letters **ea** make an /**e**/ sound in these words but they are missing. Fill in the missing letters, and then use the space provided to write the answers.

1. Tell me two things you

   spr_____d on br_____d.

   _____ _____

2. Tell me two books you've

   r_____d.

   _____ _____

3. Tell me one thing you never

   put on your h_____d.

   _____

4. Tell me one thing that is

   h_____vier than a

   f_____ther.

   _____

Flower power

Sometimes the letters **er** can sound hard as in **person**.
Sometimes the letters **er** can sound soft as in **summer**.

Look at the words on the flower's petals. Each one is missing the letters **er**. Fill in the blanks, and say the word out loud. Does the **er** sound soft or hard?

Long or short?

When you have the letters **oo**, they can make a long sound or a short sound.

The long /**oo**/ sound is in words like **food** and **zoo**.

The short /**oo**/ sound is in words like **foot** and **took**.

Fill in the missing **oo**. Then sort the words to show if they have the long /**oo**/ sound or the short /**oo**/ sound.

b_____k   b_____t   w_____d   m_____d

p_____l   g_____d   m_____n   z_____m

short /**oo**/ as in **foot** and **took**	long /**oo**/ as in **food** and **zoo**
_____	_____
_____	_____
_____	_____
_____	_____
_____	_____
_____	_____

Toad and Crow

The long /oa/ sound is sometimes written as the letters **oa**, **oe** or **ow**. You can hear the long /oa/ sound in words like **soap**, **toe** and **yellow**.

Read the story about Toad and Crow. Find the words with the long /oa/ sound (spelled **oa**, **oe** or **ow**) and draw a circle around them.

Toad looks out of his window.

Water and snow is flowing down the road!

Toad puts on his new yellow coat.

He gets in his boat and rows.

Toad meets Crow.

Crow has hurt his toe.

Toad puts Crow in the boat.

Toad goes to Crow's house.

What's in the knight's pie?

The sound **/igh/** can be written with the letters **igh** and **ie**. Say the words **sigh** and **tie** out loud. They're spelled differently, but they sound the same.

Look at the word in the knight's pie and sort them into the boxes below.

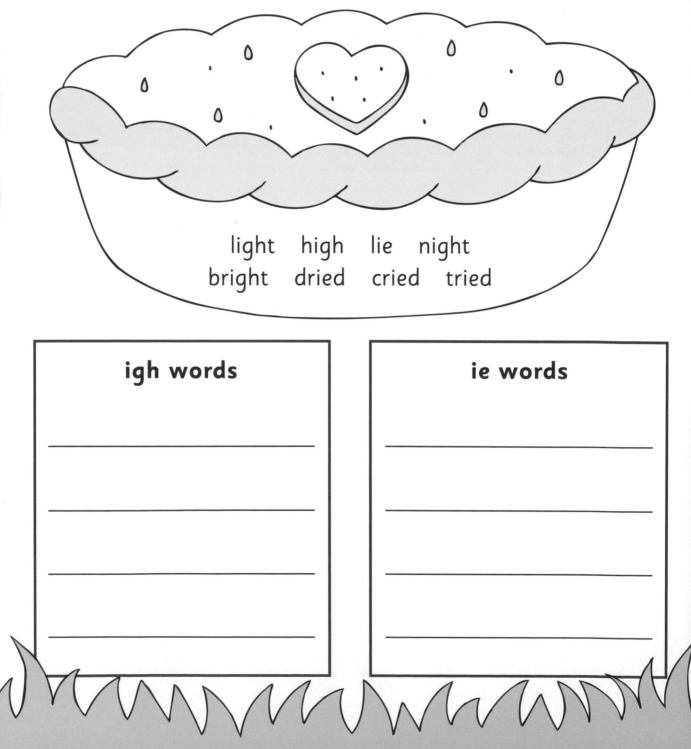

light   high   lie   night
bright   dried   cried   tried

igh words	**ie words**
_____	_____
_____	_____
_____	_____
_____	_____

The hungry dinosaur

The sound /**or**/ can be spelled in different ways:
ore as in **core**, **aw** as in **paw**, **au** as in **August**

The dinosaur is chomping all the words. Make sure they go in the right part of his tummy!

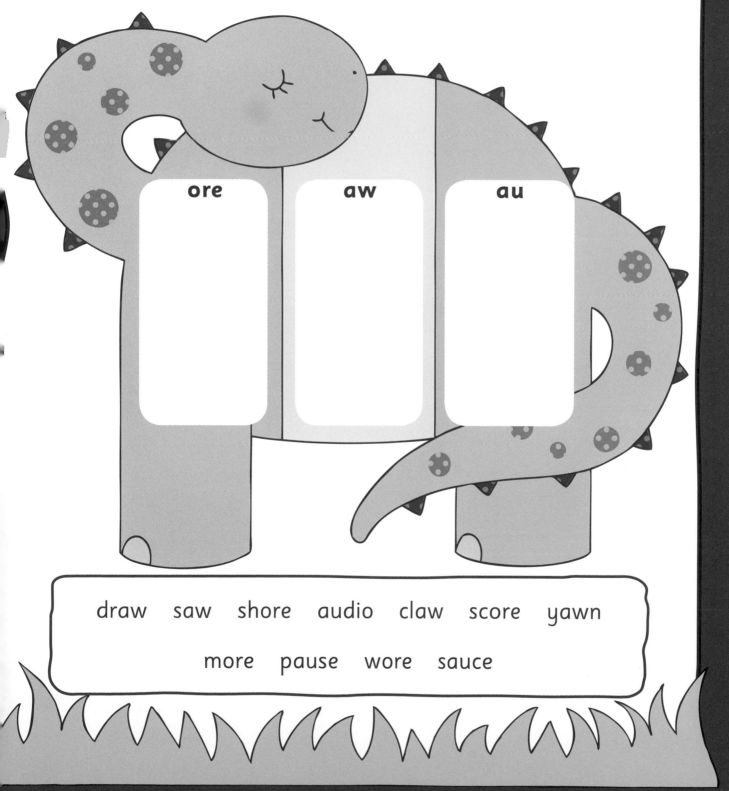

ore

aw

au

draw   saw   shore   audio   claw   score   yawn

more   pause   wore   sauce

The giant's beard

Say these words out loud.

beard   year   tear

The letters **ear** make the /**ear**/ sound.

All these words are stuck in the giant's beard. Add the missing **ear** letters. Then read each word aloud.

d_____   r_____

h_____   n_____

f_____   _____s

g_____   cl_____

sp_____

What's in the picture?

Here are three ways of spelling the **/air/** sound.

air – **chair**   **are** – **scare**   **ear** – **wear**

Say them out loud and you will hear the long **/air/** sound.

Look at the pictures and write in the missing letters with **air**, **are** or **ear**.

b_____   st_____s   p_____

h_____   t_____   ch_____

f_____y   m_____   h_____

Long sounds

Lots of words end with **y**, but they don't sound the same. With some words, the **y** makes a long /**ee**/ sound, like the word **berry**.
With other words, the **y** makes a long /**igh**/ sound, like the word **sky**.

Read the words below and say them out loud. If the word has a long /**ee**/ sound, write it under the picture of the berry. If the word has a long /**igh**/ sound, write it under the picture of the sky.

try   puppy   tiny   cry   dry   shiny   jelly   by

_____   _____

_____   _____

_____   _____

_____   _____

Missing k

In many words, the /**k**/ sound is spelled with the letter **c**, like the word **cat**. But when there is a /**k**/ sound before the letters **e**, **i** and **y**, the /**k**/ sound is spelled with the letter **k**.

key   kit   frisky

Finish the words below, by adding the **k**. Then colour in the pictures.

___ey

___ettle

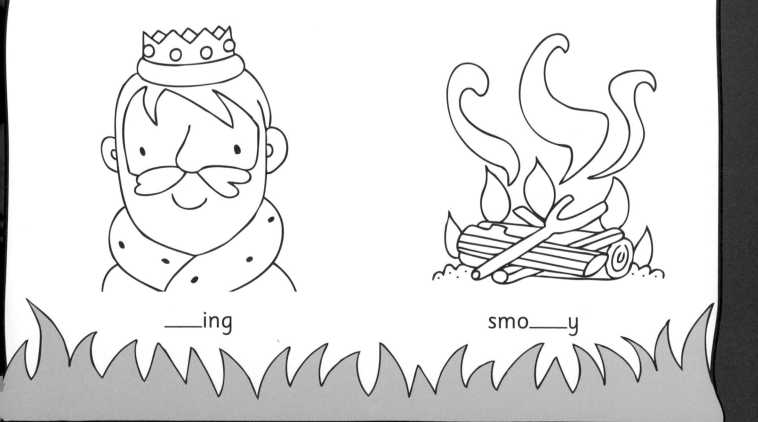

___ing

smo___y

Look, cover, say, write

Some words have tricky spellings and you need to learn how to spell them. Start by looking at the word. Which sounds are written as letters that you know? Which are different?

For example: **said**, starts with the /**s**/ sound and ends with the /**d**/ sound, but **ai** is said with the /**e**/ sound and not the /**ai**/ sound.

Look at the words below. Cover them and say them out loud. Then write them in the next box and check them.

Word	Try 1	Try 2
the		
a		
do		
to		
of		
are		
is		

Look at the words below. Cover them and say them out loud. Then write them in the next box and check them.

Word	Try 1	Try 2
was		
by		
my		
you		
one		
said		
says		
were		
your		

Spelling

Look at the words below. Cover them and say them out loud. Then write them in the next box and check them.

Word	Try 1	Try 2
once		
come		
some		
ask		
our		
today		
house		
school		
friend		

What are the animals doing?

A **verb** is a **doing** or **action** word. Read this sentence:
The dog barked.
The verb tells you what the dog is doing. So the verb is the word **barked**.

Choose the right verb to describe what each of the animals is doing.

> wagging   pecking   eating
>
> rolling   trotting   singing

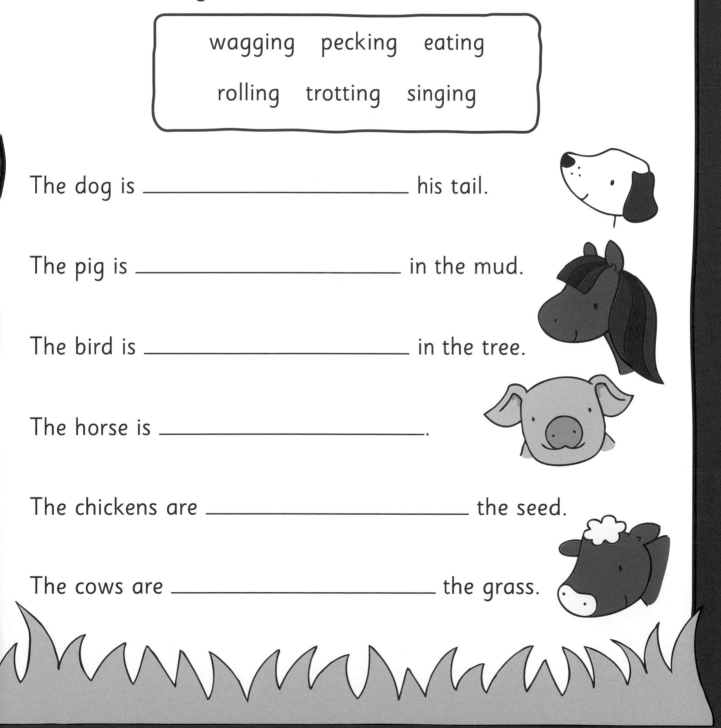

The dog is _____ his tail.

The pig is _____ in the mud.

The bird is _____ in the tree.

The horse is _____ .

The chickens are _____ the seed.

The cows are _____ the grass.

Adding ed

You can add **ed** to the end of some words (verbs, or doing words) to show that they happened in the past.

For example: **hiss + ed = hissed**

Add **ed** to these words. Do you know any more? Write them in the table below.

walk	
miss	
call	
hunt	
jump	
pull	

Adding ing

You can add **ing** to the end of some words to show that you are doing something now. For example, if you add **ing** to **I walk** you change the sentence to: **I am walking.**

Complete the story below. Add **ing** to these words and write them in the correct places.

> wear   meet   call   say   look   go

Fairy godmother was _____ "You will go to the

ball!" and waved her wand. Suddenly, Cinderella was

_____ a beautiful dress.

She arrived at the ball and everyone was _____

at her. No one knew who she was!

After _____ Prince Charming, she had fallen in

love. Just then, the clock struck midnight. She had to get

_____.

Prince Charming was _____ after her. But

she kept going even when she lost her glass slipper.

Adding er

You can change the meaning of these words by adding **er** to the end.

If you add **er** to the word **hunt**, you get the word **hunter**.

Add the missing **er** ending to these words and then write the new word in the space.

jump_____   _____

work_____   _____

read_____   _____

eat_____   _____

clean_____   _____

cook_____   _____

sing_____   _____

Done and undone

You can change the meaning of some words by adding letters to the front such as **un**. For example, if you add **un** to the word **done**, it means the opposite: **undone**.

Pat has **un**locked her case. Look at the words inside. You can add **un** to some of them, but which ones? Draw a circle around the right words.

happy   clean   key   cut
tie   top   worn   cup
car   gone   zip

Now write the words you have circled out here. Don't forget to add **un** to the beginning of each one.

_____   _____

_____   _____

_____

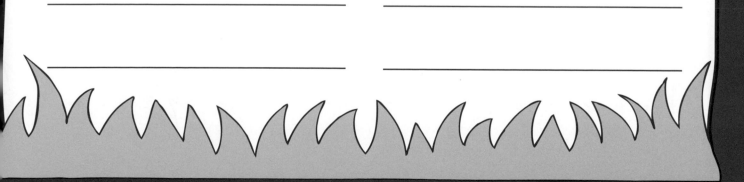

Nouns

A **noun** is a person, a place or a thing. For example: **Jo ate a lolly at the beach.**
Jo is a noun because it is a person's **name**.
Lolly is a noun because it is a **thing**.
Beach is a noun because it is a **place**.

Underline the nouns in these sentences. The clue will tell you how many.

1. The boy waited for a bus.   (2 nouns)

2. The teacher read a book.   (2 nouns)

3. The cup was broken.   (1 noun)

4. The monkey ate three bananas.   (2 nouns)

5. The dog barked at the cat.   (2 nouns)

6. The girl smiled at Grandma.   (2 nouns)

How many animals?

Plural means **more than one**. Lots of words can be made plural by adding an **s** at the end of them.

When Tom goes to the farm he can see lots of animals. If there is more than one animal, put an **s** at the end of the word.

cow____

lamb____

pig____

goat____

duck____

donkey____

There's more than one!

Many words can be made plural by adding an **s** at the end of them. But if a word ends in **x**, **ss**, **sh**, **ch** or **s** you add **es** to make it plural.

Look at all the words below. Add **es** to make each one plural, and write it on the notepad. The first one has been done for you.

~~peach~~   dish   dress   bench   glass   fox

bus   bush   box   wish   kiss   watch

peach**es**

Making sentences

A sentence usually tells us a whole thought or idea. It starts with a capital letter and ends with a full stop, question mark or exclamation mark.
Sally walked home.
This tells us who did the action (**Sally**), what the action was (**walked**) and where they went (**home**).

Look carefully at the words below. Tick the box if they make a sentence. If they don't, put a cross in the box.

☐ I like reading books.

☐ hop and skip

☐ Climbing trees is fun!

☐ Can we go to the park?

☐ dog and cat

☐ The sun is shining!

☐ Ben and Sam like ice cream.

☐ lost coat

Put them together

The word **and** is a linking word. You can use it to join two words together. For example: **black and white cat**.
Draw a line and match the words that go together. The first one has been done for you.

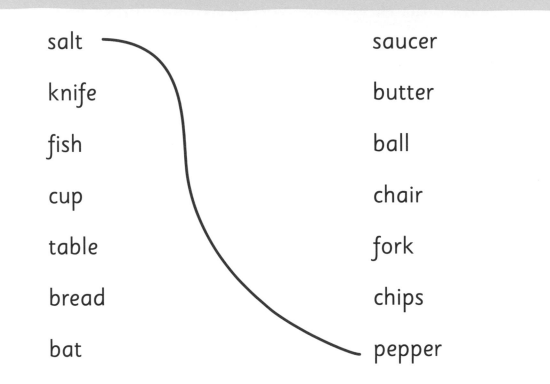

salt   saucer

knife   butter

fish   ball

cup   chair

table   fork

bread   chips

bat   pepper

Use the word and to put the two words together and write them below.

salt and pepper

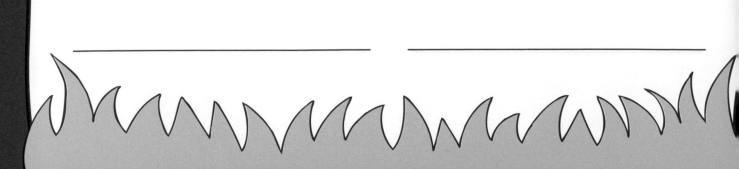

Joining up

You can use the word **and** to join two sentences together, like this:

I walked to school today. I forgot my PE kit.

I walked to school today and I forgot my PE kit.

Read the sentences below. Then join the two sentences by using the word **and**.

I saw a dog. Paul saw a cat.

_____

_____

The boys can run. The girls can jump.

_____

_____

Mum is using a hammer. Dad is using a drill.

_____

_____

What's the order?

Lucy is going to school with her dad. Write these sentences in the right order to make sure she gets there.

> Dad and I walk to school.
>
> We go into school.
>
> I say hello to my friends.
>
> I put on my shoes and coat.
>
> I say goodbye to Dad.
>
> I pick up my school bag.

1. _____

2. _____

3. _____

4. _____

5. _____

6. _____

Spaces

When you write you should always put a space between each word. The space shows where the word starts and ends.

Describe each of the pictures below.

_____

_____

_____

_____

_____

_____

_____

_____

Full stop ahead!

A sentence is a whole thought. It starts with a capital letter and usually ends with a full stop. The capital letters should be as tall as **h** or **d** and should not be joined up. Your full stop should be a small dot at the end of a sentence on the writing line.

Read the story of 'Tog the Dog'. Find the capital letters and full stops and put a ring around each one.

Tog the Dog

One day Tog the dog went out for a jog.

It was a very wet day and the path

was so muddy he fell into a bog.

Nearby was a big log and he managed

to pull himself out of the bog onto the log.

He was covered in mud and frightened a

frog sat by the bog. He had to jog all

the way home. Finally Tog the dog reached home

and sat on a log to dry.

Jumbled words

Sentences need to make sense. They should start with a capital letter and usually end with a full stop.

Put the sentence in the right order. Write your sentences on the lines underneath.

1. riding   bikes.   are   Two   boys

   _____

2. eating   ice cream.   an   is   girl   A

   _____

3. dog   The   is   the   chasing   cat.

   _____

4. old   walking   An   is   his   dog.   man

   _____

   _____

5. feeding   chicks.   her   The   is   bird

   _____

   _____

Stuck in the mud!

Sometimes we use an exclamation mark at the end of a sentence. It looks like this: **!** You use an exclamation mark to show surprise or strong feelings. For example: **Leave me alone!**

Help Rat find the capital letters by underlining them. Draw a circle around the exclamation marks.

"Help!" cried Rat. Rat was stuck in the mud, and he couldn't get out! He pulled and he pulled, but it was no good!

"Hello, Rat," said Dog. "What's the matter?"

"I'm stuck!" said Rat. "Can you pull me out?" Dog found a rope and threw it to Rat. He pulled and he pulled, but it was no good!

"Hello, Dog. Hello Rat," said Cat. "What's the matter?"

"I'm stuck!" said Rat. "Can you help pull me out?" Cat held on to Dog and they pulled the rope. They pulled and they pulled, but it was no good!

"Hello Cat and Dog. Hello Rat," said Frog. "What's the matter?"

"Rat is stuck in the mud!" said Cat and Dog. "Can you help?"

Frog held on to Cat. Cat held on to Dog. They pulled and they pulled!

POP!

Rat flew out of the mud! He landed on Frog, Cat and Dog!

Question or not?

You can use a full stop or an exclamation mark to end a sentence. If your sentence is a question, you use a question mark at the end. It looks like this: **?**
Can you help me?
You still need to use a capital letter to start the question. It is still a sentence.

These sentences are missing their capital letters and full stops or question marks. Write the capital letter and correct punctuation mark for each one. The first one has been done for you.

M   ~~m~~onkeys are funny**.**

are monkeys funny

what do pandas eat

pandas eat bamboo plants

a tiger's coat is yellow and black striped

what colour is a tiger's coat

The Clever Cockerel and the Crafty Fox

This is the story of a clever cockerel and a crafty fox, but someone has forgotten to include the capital letters, full stops, exclamation marks and question marks.

Add the capital letters, full stops, exclamation marks and question marks where they should go.

the crafty fox wanted to catch the clever cockerel so the crafty fox went to the barn where the clever cockerel lived the crafty fox put a sack over the clever cockerel the crafty fox ran off with the sack, but soon he got tired and sat down for a sleep the clever cockerel jumped out of the sack, and put a heavy stone in it when the crafty fox woke up, he picked up the sack and took it to his den he opened the sack over a pot of boiling water the heavy stone fell into the water and the boiling water splashed over the silly fox did the cockerel laugh when he heard the silly fox yell yes

My day

Another word that uses a capital letter is the word **I** (meaning myself). Remember capital letters are needed for:

- The start of sentences.
- Names of places and people.
- The word **I**.

Lisa has written all about her day. Circle the words that need a capital letter.

today i got up early. i opened my curtains and looked out of the window. it was raining! i went downstairs and i put on my coat and my boots. i ran into the garden and found lots of big puddles. i splashed in all the puddles. splash! splash! splash! then my mum told me to come inside because i was still wearing my pyjamas!

Now write about your day.

_____

_____

_____

_____

_____

Our school day

Look at the pictures and read the captions. Answer these questions.

1. What time is assembly?

_____

2. How do you know when to line up?

_____

3. What happens at 2 o'clock?

_____

The bell is rung at 9 o'clock. We line up on the playground for the register.

We have assembly at 10 o'clock.

We have playtime at 2 o'clock.

Time to go home at 3 o'clock.

The Little Red Hen

Once upon a time there was a little red hen who wanted to plant some wheat. She asked the cat to help. The cat would not help. So she planted the wheat and waited for it to grow. She asked the dog to help cut the wheat but the dog would not help. She cut it herself. She asked the pig to help grind the wheat but the pig would not help. So she did it herself. The cat, the dog and the pig did not want to help her make the bread so she did it herself. They did want to help eat the bread, but she did that all by herself!

Read the story. Then answer the questions by colouring in the right character.

1. Who wanted to plant the wheat?

2. Who would not help plant the wheat?

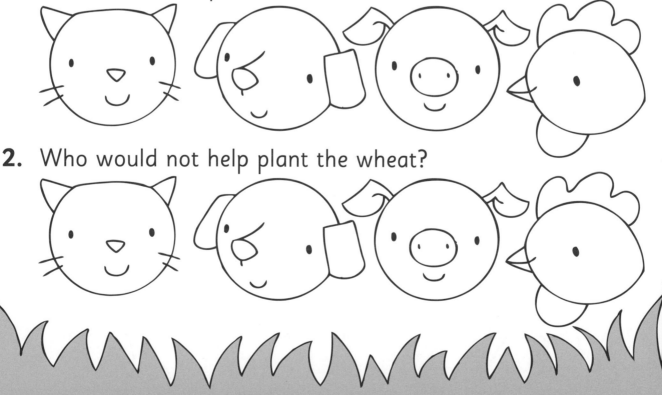

Comprehension

3. Who would not help cut the wheat?

4. Who would not help grind the wheat?

5. Who would not help make the bread?

6. Who ate the bread?

The picnic

Dan and Samir went to the park for a picnic. They packed some sandwiches, apples, bananas and water. Samir's dog came too. On the way to the park Samir ate a banana and an apple. Dan ate an apple and a banana. Samir's dog ate the sandwiches! When Samir and Dan got to the park there was only water left for their picnic. Then Samir's dog drank the water!

Answer the questions about the text.

1. Who went to the park?

_____

2. Why did they go to the park?

_____

3. What did Samir's dog eat?

_____

4. What do you think Dan and Samir did next?

_____

Comprehension

I live here!

Look at the picture of Jamal's village and read the text.

Jamal lives in a very hot, sunny place. In his village there are a few straw huts, which people live in. Children play with their animals. Jamal's family own a goat and some chickens. It is so hot they do not need to wear many clothes. Food is cooked outside, over a fire.

Now circle the right word to answer the questions. The first one has been done for you.

1. Where does Jamal live?

   Jamal lives in a **hot** / **cold** place.

2. What are the huts made of?

   The huts are made of **bricks** / **straw**.

3. What do the children play with?

   Children play with their **dolls** / **animals**.

4. What animals do Jamal's family own?

   Jamal's family own a **dog** / **goat** and some

   chickens / **fish**.

Sam the dog

Read what it says about Sam the dog.

The dog has short brown fur and a tail. He is small with pointed ears. He has a red collar and his name is Sam. He likes to sleep in his basket by the window. But he barks loudly when the postman comes down the path.

Answer the questions below. Match the question with the answer.

What colour is the dog's fur?		red
Is the dog small or big?		basket
What colour is the dog's collar?		brown
Where does the dog sleep?		postman
Who does the dog bark at?		small

Growing sunflowers

Read all about how to grow a sunflower.

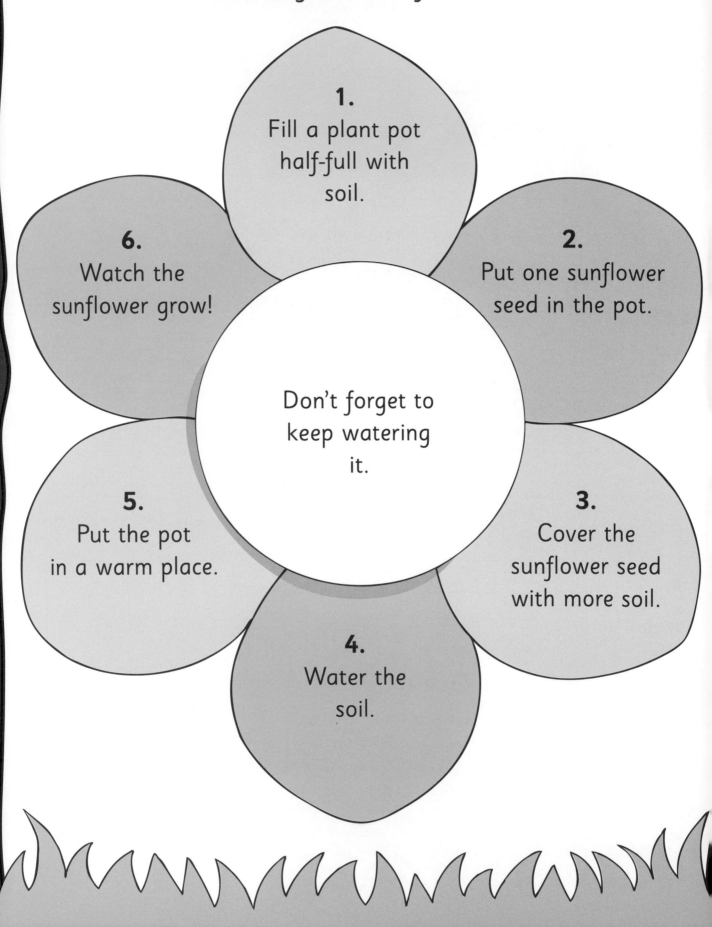

1.
Fill a plant pot half-full with soil.

2.
Put one sunflower seed in the pot.

3.
Cover the sunflower seed with more soil.

4.
Water the soil.

5.
Put the pot in a warm place.

6.
Watch the sunflower grow!

Don't forget to keep watering it.

Circle the right answer to these questions.

1. What do you put the sunflower seed in?

   a bag   a pot   a jar

2. What do you put in the pot first?

   soil   sand   rice

3. How many sunflower seeds are in the pot?

   two   four   one

4. Where do you put the pot?

   a cold place   a warm place   a dark place

5. What do you think will happen if you don't water it?

   _____

   _____

   _____

   _____

What would you like?

Choose two things for Max and two things for Mary.
Write in the boxes what Max and Mary said to the
waitress. Here are some words to help you:

beans   toast   please   like   burger   would

I   chips   fruit juice   hot dog   milkshake

Max

Mary

What are they saying?

Match the sentences to the right picture. Write the sentences in the bubbles.

> Oh Grandma, what big eyes you have!
>
> Put me back together again!
>
> Have you any wool?

Composition

The alien planet

Describe this picture. The words below will help you.

near   inside   in front of   beside
down   across   behind

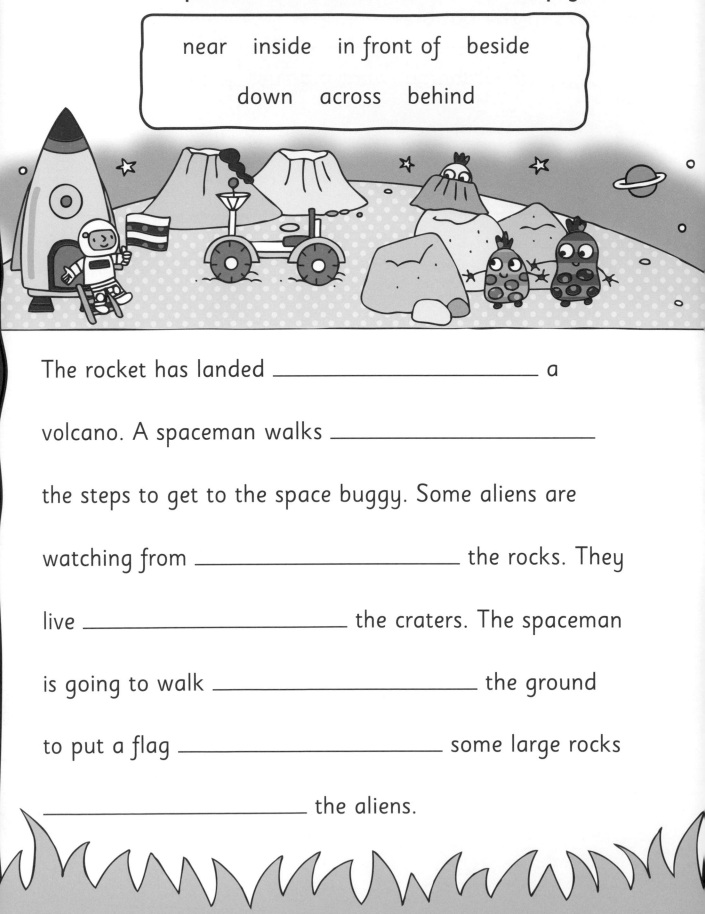

The rocket has landed _____ a

volcano. A spaceman walks _____

the steps to get to the space buggy. Some aliens are

watching from _____ the rocks. They

live _____ the craters. The spaceman

is going to walk _____ the ground

to put a flag _____ some large rocks

_____ the aliens.

What did they say?

Look at the pictures showing the story of The Three Billy Goats Gruff. Using short sentences, write in the speech bubbles what the goats and the troll might be saying.

Clean your teeth!

Read the sentences and put them in order. Write a number next to each sentence. Put number 1 next to the first thing you do when you clean your teeth. Number 6 will be the last thing you do.

What colour is your toothbrush? Colour in the toothbrush to match yours.

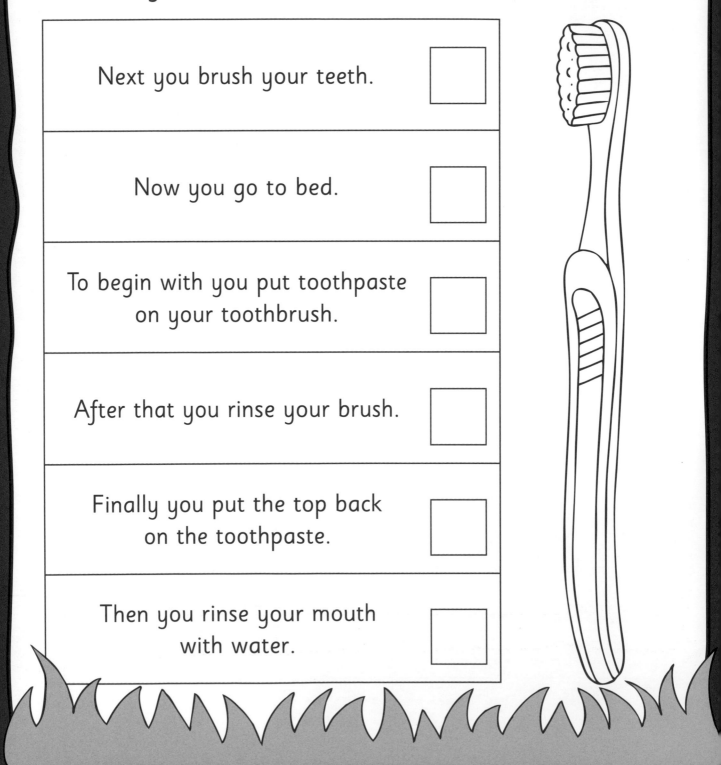

Next you brush your teeth. ☐

Now you go to bed. ☐

To begin with you put toothpaste on your toothbrush. ☐

After that you rinse your brush. ☐

Finally you put the top back on the toothpaste. ☐

Then you rinse your mouth with water. ☐

Ben and Tim write a letter

Ben and Tim are on holiday. Here is a list of what they did, but it's all muddled up.

Write the sentences in the right order on the letter they are sending to their granny.

> Then we went to a castle. Tim got splashed by a wave!
>
> First, we got up and had breakfast.
>
> After the castle, we went to the beach.

_____

_____

_____

_____

_____

_____

Love from _____

Progress chart

Making progress? Tick (✔) the flower boxes as you complete each section of the book.

Spelling

Vocabulary

Punctuation

Composition

Grammar

Comprehension

Well done!

YOU DID IT! ★

Name: _____

You have completed **YEAR 1 ENGLISH** Practice Book

Age: _____   Date: _____

Answers

The answers are given below. They are referenced by page number and where applicable, question number. The answers usually only include the information the children are expected to give.

Note that answers in literacy will be varied and subjective from child to child, and a fair degree of marker discretion and interpretation is needed, particularly if children's understanding and skills have to be deduced from their answers.

Page number	Question number	Answers
6		doll, duck, sniff, grass, buzz
7		rabbit – 2, butterfly – 3, crocodile – 3, elephant – 3, caterpillar – 4
8		r**ay**, sn**ai**l, b**oy**, c**oi**n
9		b**ake**, g**ame**, sn**ake**, sh**ape**, t**ake**, sk**ate**
10		
11		note, stone, hope, nose
12		**Cube ('u–e' words):** cute, huge, tune, rule, fuse, tube **Glue ('ue' words):** blue, true, due, clue, cue
13		need, peas, seal, chief, wheel, peel, easy, tea, team, piece, deep
14		spr**ea**d, br**ea**d, r**ea**d, h**ea**d, h**ea**vier, f**ea**ther
15		p**er**son, scoot**er**, riv**er**, h**er**b, farm**er**, v**er**b, t**er**m, h**er**, flow**er** **Soft 'er' sound:** scooter, her, flower, river, farmer **Hard 'er' sound:** person, herb, term, verb
16		b**oo**k, b**oo**t, w**oo**d, m**oo**d, p**oo**l, g**oo**d, m**oo**n, z**oo**m **Short /oo/:** book, wood, good **Long /oo/:** boot, pool, moon, mood, zoom
17		The following words should be circled: Toad, window, snow, road, Toad, yellow, coat, boat, rows, Toad, Crow, Crow, toe, Toad, Crow, boat, Toad, Crow's
18		**'igh' words:** light, high, night, bright **'ie' words:** lie, dried, cried, tried
19		**'ore' words:** shore, score, more, wore **'aw' words:** draw, saw, claw, yawn **'au' words:** audio, pause, sauce
20		d**ear**, r**ear**, h**ear**, n**ear**, f**ear**, **ear**s, g**ear**, cl**ear**, sp**ear**
21		b**ear**, st**air**s, p**ear**, h**are**, t**ear**, ch**air**, f**air**y, m**are**, h**air**

Page number	Question number	Answers
22		**Strawberry (long /ee/):** puppy, shiny, jelly, tiny **Sky (long /igh/ sound):** try, cry, dry, by
23		key, kettle, king, smoky
24		Children's own answers.
25		Children's own answers.
26		Children's own answers.
27		wagging, rolling, singing, trotting, pecking, eating
28		walked, missed, called, hunted, jumped, pulled
29		saying, wearing, looking, meeting, going, calling
30		jumper, worker, reader, eater, cleaner, cooker, singer
31		The following words should be circled: happy, clean, cut, tie, worn, zip **un**happy, **un**clean, **un**cut, **un**tie, **un**worn, **un**zip
32	1	The <u>boy</u> waited for a <u>bus</u>.
	2	The <u>teacher</u> read a <u>book</u>.
	3	The <u>cup</u> was broken.
	4	The <u>monkey</u> ate three <u>bananas</u>.
	5	The <u>dog</u> barked at the <u>cat</u>.
	6	The <u>girl</u> smiled at <u>Grandma</u>.
33		cow**s**, lamb**s**, pig**s**, goat**s**, duck**s**, donkey**s**
34		peach**es**, dish**es**, dress**es**, bench**es**, glass**es**, fox**es**, bus**es**, bush**es**, box**es**, wish**es**, kiss**es**, watch**es**
35		I like reading books. ✓ hop and skip ✗ Climbing trees is fun! ✓ Can we go to the park? ✓ dog and cat ✗ The sun is shining! ✓ Ben and Sam like ice cream. ✓ lost coat ✗
36		salt – pepper, knife – fork, fish – chips, cup – saucer, table – chair, bread – butter, bat – ball salt and pepper, knife and fork, fish and chips, cup and saucer, table and chair, bread and butter, bat and ball
37		I saw a dog and Paul saw a cat. The boys can run and the girls can jump. Mum is using a hammer and Dad is using a drill.
38		1. I put on my shoes and coat. 2. I pick up my school bag. 3. Dad and I walk to school. 4. We go into school. 5. I say hello to my friends. 6. I say goodbye to Dad. Points 5 and 6 can be in a different order (a child might say goodbye to their parent before saying hello to their friends).
39		Children's own answers, with a space between each word.

Page number	Question number	Answers
40		Tog the Dog One day Tog the dog went out for a jog. It was a very wet day and the path was so muddy he fell into a bog. Nearby was a big log and he managed to pull himself out of the bog onto the log. He was covered in mud and frightened a frog sat by the bog. He had to jog all the way home. Finally Tog the dog reached home and sat on a log to dry.
41		Two boys are riding bikes. A girl is eating an ice cream. The dog is chasing the cat. An old man is walking his dog. The bird is feeding her chicks.
42		"Help!" cried Rat. Rat was stuck in the mud, and he couldn't get out! He pulled and he pulled, but it was no good! "Hello, Rat," said Dog. "What's the matter?" "I'm stuck!" said Rat. "Can you pull me out?" Dog found a rope and threw it to Rat. He pulled and he pulled, but it was no good! "Hello, Dog. Hello Rat," said Cat. "What's the matter?" "I'm stuck!" said Rat. "Can you pull me out?" Cat held on to Dog and they pulled the rope. They pulled and they pulled, but it was no good! "Hello Cat and Dog. Hello Rat," said Frog. "What's the matter?" "Rat is stuck in the mud!" said Cat and Dog. "Can you help?" Frog held on to Cat. Cat held on to Dog. They pulled and they pulled! POP! Rat flew out of the mud! He landed on Frog, Cat and Dog!
43		Monkeys are funny. Are monkeys funny? What do pandas eat? Pandas eat bamboo plants. A tiger's coat is yellow and black striped. What colour is a tiger's coat?
44		The crafty fox wanted to catch the clever cockerel. So the crafty fox went to the barn where the clever cockerel lived. The crafty fox put a sack over the clever cockerel! The crafty fox ran off with the sack, but soon he got tired and sat down for a sleep. The clever cockerel jumped out of the sack, and put a heavy stone in it! When the crafty fox woke up, he picked up the sack and took it to his den. He opened the sack over a pot of boiling water! The heavy stone fell into the water and the boiling water splashed over the silly fox! Did the cockerel laugh when he heard the silly fox yell? Yes! (Children may choose to place exclamation marks in different places.)

Page number	Question number	Answers
45		The following letters in bold should be circled:
		today **i** got up early. **i** opened my curtains and looked out of the window. **i**t was raining! **i** went downstairs and **i** put on my coat and my boots. **i** ran into the garden and found lots of big puddles. **i** splashed in all the puddles. **s**plash! **s**plash! **s**plash! **t**hen my mum told me to come inside because **i** was still wearing my pyjamas!
		Children's own answers.
46	1	10 o'clock
	2	the bell is rung
	3	playtime
47	1	hen
	2	cat
48	3	dog
	4	pig
	5	cat, dog and pig
	6	hen
49	1	Dan and Samir
	2	for a picnic
	3	sandwiches
	4	Children's own answers.
50	1	hot
	2	straw
	3	animals
	4	goat, chickens
51		What colour is the dog's fur? – brown, Is the dog small or big? – small, What colour is the dog's collar? – red, Where does the dog sleep? – basket, Who does the dog bark at? – postman
53	1	a pot
	2	soil
	3	one
	4	a warm place
	5	Children's own answers.
54		Children's own answers.
55		Humpty Dumpty by the wall – Put me back together again!
		Boy and sheep – Have you any wool?
		Red Riding Hood at grandma's house – Oh Grandma, what big eyes you have!
56		near, down, behind, inside, across, in front of, beside
57		Children's own answers.
58		1. To begin with you put toothpaste on your toothbrush.
		2. Next you brush your teeth.
		3. Then you rinse your mouth with water.
		4. After that you rinse your brush.
		5. Finally you put the top back on the toothpaste.
		6. Now you go to bed.
59		First, we got up and had breakfast.
		Then we went to a castle.
		After the castle, we went to the beach.
		Tim got splashed by a wave!